This
HOW TO TRAIN YOUR DRAGON
ANNUAL 2020
belongs to:

....

....

EGMONT
We bring stories to life

First published in Great Britain
in 2019 by Egmont UK Limited,
The Yellow Building, 1 Nicholas Road, London
W11 4AN

Content written and adapted
by Rebecca Oku and Helen Archer
Designed by Jeannette O'Toole

DreamWorks Dragons© 2019
DreamWorks Animation LLC.
All rights reserved.
ISBN 978 1 4052 9427 0
70382/001

Egmont takes its responsibility
to the planet and its inhabitants very
seriously. We aim to use papers
from well-managed forests run by
responsible suppliers.

Printed in Italy

HOW TO TRAIN YOUR
DRAGON
ANNUAL 2020

CONTENTS

THE BEGINNING ... 8

MEET THE VIKINGS – Hiccup 14

MEET THE VIKINGS – Astrid 15

DRAGON MAZE 16

MEET THE VIKINGS –
Valka, Fishlegs, Snotlout 18

MEET THE VIKINGS –
Eret, Tuffnut, Ruffnut 19

HERO HICCUP 20

SUDOKU 21

SPOT THE DIFFERENCE 22

PICTURE MIX-UP 23

STORY: Hidden World Part 1 24

MEET THE DRAGONS – Toothless 28

MEET THE DRAGONS –
Lightfury, Night Lights 29

THE DRAGONS OF BERK –
Search and Find 30

ODD DRAGON OUT 31

MEET THE DRAGONS –
Stormfly, Hookfang, Meatlug 32

MEET THE DRAGONS –
Barf and Belch, Skullcrusher, Cloudjumper 33

WHICH VIKING IS THIS?	**34**
POSTERS	**35**
BERK SEARCH	**39**
DANCE OF THE DRAGONS	**40**
WHICH DRAGON RIDER ARE YOU?	**42**
STORY: Hidden World Part 2	**44**
QUICK-FIRE QUIZ	**48**
TAKE FLIGHT	**49**
FISHLEGS' DRAGONS FACTS	**50**
DRAGON CARDS	**51**
FLYING FRIENDS	**57**
OFF TO BATTLE	**58**
DRAGON MIX-UP	**60**
SECRET MESSAGE	**60**
MATCH THE PAIR	**61**
DRAW TOOTHLESS	**62**
COMPLETE THE SEQUENCE	**64**
POSTERS	**65**
SHAPES AND SIZES	**67**
ANSWERS	**68**

DREAMWORKS

HOW TO TRAIN YOUR

DRAGON

THE BEGINNING ...

Introducing Hiccup, Berk's worst Viking.
He was small and weak and could barely lift a sword, let alone use one. Worst of all, he was the only Viking who hadn't fought a dragon.

Hiccup lived in the small town of Berk, home to his Viking clan. He was the son of Stoick the Vast, the chief of Berk and a famed dragon slayer. But he was not very much like his father.

Thankfully Hiccup was clever and a very good inventor, so he found a way to bring peace to Berk and solve the dragon problem.

HE BECAME A DRAGON RIDER!

Becoming a Dragon Rider was not something he set out to do.
In fact, he was very scared of dragons.
That is until he met a Night Fury.
Night Furies are the fastest and once feared to be the most dangerous of all dragons. They have supersonic speed, so catching one is almost impossible.
But Hiccup managed it.

Hiccup caught the Night Fury with one of his inventions, the Mangler, injuring its tail fin.

He founds where the dragon had fallen and was sad to see it injured and unable to fly. Hiccup realised that dragons weren't as ferocious as he'd been led to believe.

Hiccup named the Night Fury, Toothless and built him a new tail fin. Hiccup slowly trained Toothless, teaching him how to fly with his help and they soon became friends.

Hiccup and Toothless had to work together to show the Vikings that dragons can be friends. With the help of Hiccup's friends and a few more dragons, they defeated the Red Death and even convinced Stoick that dragons are good.

Thanks to Hiccup and Toothless' friendship, after seven generations of battling, Vikings and dragons began to live in harmony in Berk.

Toothless and Hiccup faced brand new challenges when Stoick told Hiccup it was time for him to become Chief. Hiccup didn't want to take on that responsibility. He would much rather have kept exploring their kingdom with Astrid and their dragons.

On one of their adventures, the pair met Eret, a dragon trapper. He told Hiccup that he was working for a dragon hunter called Drago Bludvist who was building a dragon army to control all dragons. Eret tried to capture Toothless and Astrid's dragon, Stormfly. They narrowly escaped and retreated to Berk to warn everyone.

Knowing Drago's history, Stoick ordered the clan to prepare for battle but Hiccup refused to listen and flew off with Toothless to talk to Drago.

As Hiccup and Toothless scoured the skies, they were confronted by a mysterious masked warrior and a fearsome dragon. The dragon grabbed Hiccup, and Toothless fell into the sea without Hiccup to control his tail fin.

The warrior took Hiccup to a dragon sanctuary and revealed herself to be Valka, Hiccup's long-lost mother. Valka told Hiccup how she came to rescue and train dragons and, after reuniting him with Toothless, she showed them the home she had built for rescued dragons.

Meanwhile, Astrid and her friends had snuck out of Berk to look for Hiccup. They found Eret and went with him to meet Drago. Drago showed them his Bewilderbeast, an Alpha dragon that controled his dragon army. Drago used the Alpha to turn their dragons against them.

Astrid tried to scare Drago by telling him about the Dragon Riders of Berk, but that only gave him the idea to conquer Berk too, and he set off to take it.

Meanwhile, Valka showed Hiccup the dragons she had rescued from hunters and how she lived among them. Hiccup hoped that she'd help him find Drago and stop his army. But, before he could ask her, his father, Stoick arrived to rescue him. Stoick has not seen his wife since Hiccup was a baby and they were very happy to be reunited.

Just then the dragon sanctuary was attacked!

Drago and his army attacked Valka's rescued dragons, forcing them into battle. Valka called the Bewilderbeast, a huge white Alpha dragon, to protect the dragons, but Drago had a Bewilderbeast of his own and the two powerful creatures fought. The riders knew that whichever dragon won would have control over all the dragons. Valka's dragon was defeated by Drago's and all the dragons fell under his control, including Toothless.

Toothless was ordered to attack Hiccup. Stoick dove in front of Hiccup as Toothless released his plasma blast and was killed. For a moment, Toothless was released from the Alpha's control and realised what had happened. Rejected by Hiccup, Toothless fell back under Drago's control as Drago ordered him and the dragon army to attack Berk.

The grieving Dragon Riders hurried to Berk to confront Drago, flying there on the baby dragons (who are immune to the Alpha's control) from the sanctuary. Hiccup used his powerful bond with Toothless to free him from the Alpha's control. Reunited, the pair took on Drago and the Bewilderbeast and Toothless became the new Alpha. Berk and the dragons were saved.

Saddened by his father's death, but with his mother and his friends to support him, Hiccup realised that it is time he became Chief.

Continue
the story on page 24,
THE HIDDEN WORLD

MEET THE VIKINGS

HICCUP

- **HICCUP** is Chief of Berk and the first Viking on Berk to train a dragon.

- He is best friends with his dragon **TOOTHLESS**. They make a formidable team against dragon hunters.

- He makes a new tail fin for **TOOTHLESS** so that he can fly with a rider.

- **HICCUP** is brave and kind. He couldn't kill a dragon like his clan used to do. He's the reason they became Dragon Riders instead.

Who's Hiccup flying with in this jigsaw? Trace over the dots to find out.

Toothless

ASTRID

- **ASTRID** is a strong and confident Viking.

- She gives Hiccup advice and support about decision-making in Berk. He trusts her more than anyone else.

- **ASTRID** was one of the first Vikings to become a Dragon Rider after Hiccup showed her how to train dragons.

- She discovers the Hidden World with Hiccup.

Colour in this picture of Astrid's dragon. Trace over the dots to spell her name.

Stormfly

DRAGON MAZE

Hiccup and Astrid have lost their dragons in the woods. Help them get them back by finding the path that brings them to Toothless and Stormfly.

START

FINISH

MEET THE VIKINGS

VALKA

- **VALKA** is Hiccup's mother and a fierce Dragon Rider.

- She is passionate about protecting dragons and will do anything to free them from dragon hunters.

- Her dragon is

> Cloudjumper

FISHLEGS

- **FISHLEGS** knows all there is to know about dragons. He's read the BOOK OF DRAGONS seven times.

- He doesn't like to get in trouble but will break any rules when it comes to helping his friends.

- His dragon is

> Meatlug

SNOTLOUT

- **SNOTLOUT** may be one of the most arrogant Vikings in Berk, but he loves his friends and would do anything to protect them.

- He thinks he is the best at saving dragons (but he's not).

- His dragon is

> Hookfang

ERET

- **ERET** used to be a dragon trapper but Hiccup and the Dragon Riders convinced him to train dragons instead.

- He is an intimidating Viking and a great warrior in battle.

- His dragon is

Skullcrusher

RUFFNUT AND TUFFNUT

- **RUFFNUT** and **TUFFNUT** are the most mischievous Vikings in Berk.

- They're always bickering but wouldn't be without each other. That's why their two-headed dragon is perfect for them.

- Their dragon is

Barf and Belch

HERO HICCUP

Hiccup is one of Berk's heroes. He's so brave that he even fights with a burning sword. Help Hiccup prepare for battle by colouring in the picture.

SUDOKU

Can you help the Vikings solve this sudoku?
Fill in all the rows with the numbers 1-4 without
repeating the same number in
each row and column.

Answers on page 68.

SPOT THE DIFFERENCE

Can you find the eight differences in the scene below? Circle all the differences in the second picture.

Answers on page 68.

22

PICTURE MIX-UP

Put the picture back together in the right order to reveal which Dragon is ready to fly.

HOW TO TRAIN YOUR
DRAGON
THE HIDDEN WORLD

STORY PART 1

AFTER DEFEATING DRAGO, Hiccup and the Vikings of Berk wanted to keep helping trapped dragons and so they often fought trappers and freed dragons from their cages, inviting them to live on Berk. Soon, the skies above the small village of Berk were filled with dragons.

"It's too crowded," Gobber told Hiccup. "And the trappers are closing in on us."

"We can handle them," Hiccup retorted. "After all, we have the Alpha dragon."

Hiccup had made many enemies. The trappers were angry that they had lost so many dragons and wanted revenge. They hired a dragon hunter, called Grimmel, who set a trap for Toothless using a Light Fury as bait.

One night, Toothless heard a strange sound and went to investigate. He found a beautiful white dragon in the forest.

Toothless and the Light Fury were captivated by each other and she warned him that there was a trap so that he could escape.

Grimmel's plan had failed, but Eret warned Hiccup. "He's the smartest dragon hunter I've ever met and he'll be back."

Hiccup loved Berk but he realised it was no longer safe. He gathered the Vikings and told them of the Hidden World his father Stoick had described – a place where nobody would ever find them.

"Out there beyond the sunset lies the home of the dragons …" Stoick used to say. So the Vikings of Berk took to the skies in search of the Hidden World.

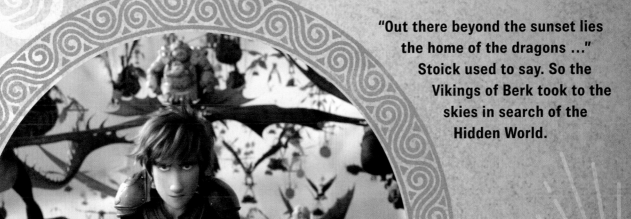

Along the way, they found an island with lush forests, gushing waterfalls and soaring cliffs. The Vikings immediately named it New Berk. But Hiccup warned them that it was only temporary. They had to find the Hidden World.

Realising that Toothless wanted to find the Light Fury and fly on his own, Hiccup unpacked his tools and made a new tail fin that Toothless could operate without Hiccup's help.
"Go get your girl," Hiccup said to Toothless.

Toothless flew off by himself looking for the Light Fury. When he found her, she showed him that she could camouflage herself and seemingly disappear into thin air! Toothless followed her into the clouds and over the seas ...

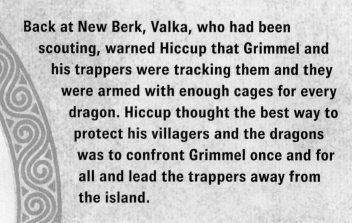

Back at New Berk, Valka, who had been scouting, warned Hiccup that Grimmel and his trappers were tracking them and they were armed with enough cages for every dragon. Hiccup thought the best way to protect his villagers and the dragons was to confront Grimmel once and for all and lead the trappers away from the island.

Hiccup and the Dragon Riders flew to an old fort, but when they arrived Grimmel was waiting for them with his terrifying Deathgripper dragons.

"You're nothing without your dragon," Grimmel sneered at Hiccup as his Deathgrippers prepared to strike. Quick as a flash, Valka summoned her dragon, Cloudjumper, who helped them to escape back to Berk.

Toothless had still not returned, so Hiccup and Astrid took Stormfly to help them find him. They flew over the seas until they reached an enormous caldera in the middle of the sea. They dived down into it and discovered a huge underground cavern.

They had reached **THE HIDDEN WORLD.**

The STORY continues on **PAGE 44.**

MEET THE DRAGONS

TOOTHLESS

TOOTHLESS is a Night Fury and one of the most fearless dragons.

He is a fierce and loyal protector of his human best friend Hiccup.

As the last of his kind, Toothless is extremely rare and a prime target for dragon hunters.

He has retractable teeth and supersonic speed. Rather than fire, he shoots plasma blasts.

Colour in Toothless's Dragon Class symbol, **STRIKE**.

LIGHT FURY

- **LIGHT FURY** loves to be free and doesn't want a rider but meeting Toothless shows her that humans can be friendly.

- With her iridescent scales, **LIGHT FURY** can blend into clouds and sky during the day.

- **LIGHT FURY** is gentle and playful by nature but is fierce when in danger.

- Like Toothless, **LIGHT FURY** flies at supersonic speeds and uses her plasma blasts to defend and disguise herself.

NIGHT LIGHTS

- The **NIGHT LIGHTS** are the adorable offspring of the TOOTHLESS and the LIGHT FURY.

- Like their parents, they can use their own plasma blasts to transform their scales into mirror-like reflectors and they have retractable teeth.

- The **NIGHT LIGHTS** are playful and curious and so are often up to mischief!

THE DRAGONS OF BERK
SEARCH AND FIND

The dragons are competing with their riders in Berk's sheep toss. Help the dragons win the game by finding all the sheep in the picture. Write how many you found in the box below.

HINT: There's one BLACK sheep to find too!

____ SHEEP

Answers on page 68.

ODD DRAGON OUT

Help Fishlegs put the symbols in the correct sequence by drawing the missing symbol in the boxes below.

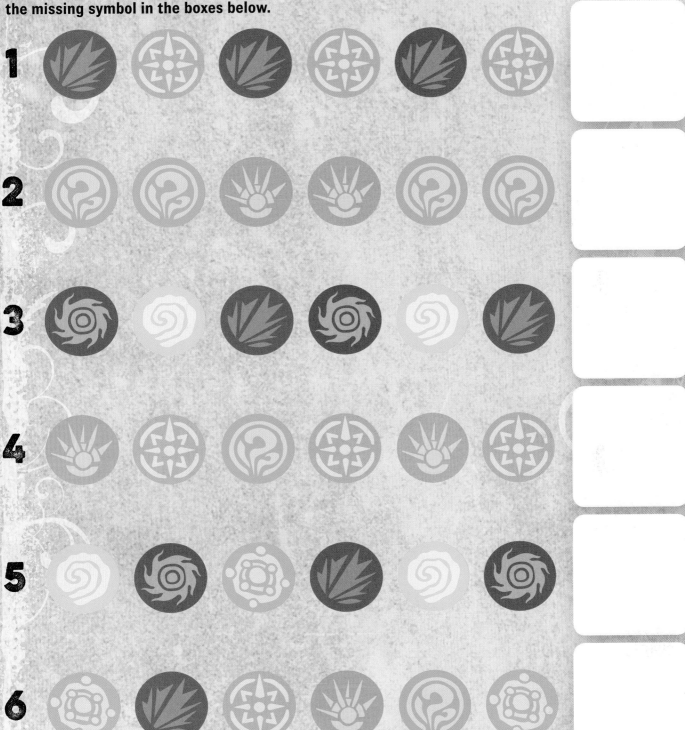

1

2

3

4

5

6

Answers on page 68.

STORMFLY

- **STORMFLY** is ASTRID'S dragon and one of the fastest fliers.

- She loves to keep her scales clean and is often found grooming herself.

- Like ASTRID, she is not afraid of conflict and is always one of the first dragons to get involved in the action.

HOOKFANG

- **HOOKFANG** is just like his rider SNOTLOUT – they're both very stubborn!

- He's also very mischievous and often ignores SNOTLOUT'S orders.

- **HOOKFANG** is one of the most aggressive dragons and can ignite his whole body in self-defence, making him especially fearsome in battle.

MEATLUG

- **MEATLUG** is not only FISHLEGS' dragon but his best friend. The two are almost never apart.

- She loves to have belly rubs and hang out with FISHLEGS whilst he researches dragons.

- **MEATLUG** can shoot flaming rocks and lava.

BARF AND BELCH

- Like their riders, **BARF** and **BELCH** don't get along and are often knocking heads – literally!

- They're happiest when flying with **RUFFNUT** and **TUFFNUT**, biting their own tails and blasting fire.

SKULLCRUSHER

- **SKULLCRUSHER** used to be STOICK'S dragon, but after he died, this dragon found a new rider, ERET.

- **SKULLCRUSHER** is a Rumblehorn dragon with a strong sense of smell. Eret relies on this to track humans and dragons alike.

CLOUDJUMPER

- **CLOUDJUMPER** gained his rider, VALKA, when he captured her from the village of Berk.

- **CLOUDJUMPER** uses X-wing flight and shoots fire in a spiral pattern.

- VALKA and **CLOUDJUMPER** worked together for years helping rescue dragons from trappers.

Can you work out which Viking is in this torn up picture? Write your answer in the box below.

Answers on page 68.

THE **MYTH** IS REAL

GOTTA KEEP
FLYING!

CUT ALONG HERE

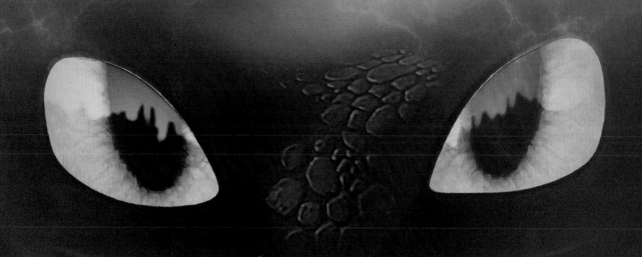

LIGHT UP
THE NIGHT

SUIT UP, GANG!

BERK SEARCH

The Dragon Riders and their dragons are hiding in this wordsearch. Find their names by looking forwards, backwards, up, down and diagonally.

F	N	G	N	A	F	K	O	O	H	E	N
R	M	A	L	S	S	E	D	O	P	G	A
A	U	S	N	O	T	L	O	U	T	R	D
B	S	T	K	J	X	P	U	C	C	I	H
H	T	O	X	U	E	E	Y	S	R	M	E
R	G	R	T	H	A	E	R	T	H	M	L
I	U	M	U	W	O	F	S	N	M	E	P
B	L	F	F	O	V	A	L	K	A	L	T
H	T	L	F	S	G	E	L	H	S	I	F
P	A	Y	N	N	D	H	C	L	E	B	K
L	E	W	U	T	U	R	G	A	T	M	E
S	M	X	T	O	O	T	H	L	E	S	S

HICCUP
ASTRID
TOOTHLESS
VALKA
RUFFNUT
TUFFNUT
SNOTLOUT
FISHLEGS
TOOTHLESS
STORMFLY
BARF
BELCH
MEATLUG
HOOKFANG

Can you spot the name of someone who doesn't belong in Berk?

G _ _ _ _ _ _ _

Answers on page 68.

39

DANCE OF THE DRAGONS

The dragons may have Viking riders but they are always ready to follow their Alpha, Toothless, into battle against the trappers!

Study the picture, then cover it over. Can you answer the following questions without checking? Try testing your friends too!

1 How many dragons are in the picture?

5 ☐   6 ☐

2 What colour is Hookfang?

GREEN ☐   RED ☐

3 How many spikes does Stormfly have on her head?

12 ☐   10 ☐

4 How many tails do Barf and Belch have?

1 ☐   2 ☐

5 What colour are Toothless's eyes?

GREEN ☐   BLUE ☐

Answers on page 68.

WHICH DRAGON RIDER ARE YOU?

There are lots of different Dragon Riders in Berk. Answer the questions to find out which one you are most like.

YES

Are you a NATURAL LEADER?

YES

NO

START HERE

Are you a QUICK LEARNER?

NO

Do you like to CAUSE MISCHIEF?

YES

YES

Are you a GREAT INVENTOR?

HICCUP

NO

ASTRID

YES

Do you love to look after BABY DRAGONS?

FISHLEGS

NO

SNOTLOUT

NO

Are you bad at FOLLOWING ORDERS?

RUFFNUT

YES

TUFFNUT

DreamWorks
HOW TO TRAIN YOUR
DRAGON
THE HIDDEN WORLD

HICCUP AND ASTRID had found the Hidden World. They were surrounded by dragons of all types and sizes in an underground cave lit up by bioluminescent crystals. "It really does exist!" said Hiccup.

Hiccup and Astrid spotted Toothless and the Light Fury on an island. All the dragons were bowing down to them. Toothless truly was the Alpha of all dragons.

Just then, the dragons spotted the humans and readied themselves to attack. Toothless commanded them to stop, and he and Stormfly took Hiccup and Astrid back to New Berk. They were followed by the Light Fury. But when they arrived at New Berk, they realised that Grimmel had found it too.

Grimmel fired a tranquiliser dart at the Light Fury. Toothless unleashed a plasma blast but it was too late, he was struck by a dart. Grimmel then captured the Alpha, and chained Toothless to his airship. Hiccup and the Vikings could only watch in horror as their beloved dragons followed Grimmel.

"We're going to get them back!" cried Hiccup. **"SUIT UP!"**

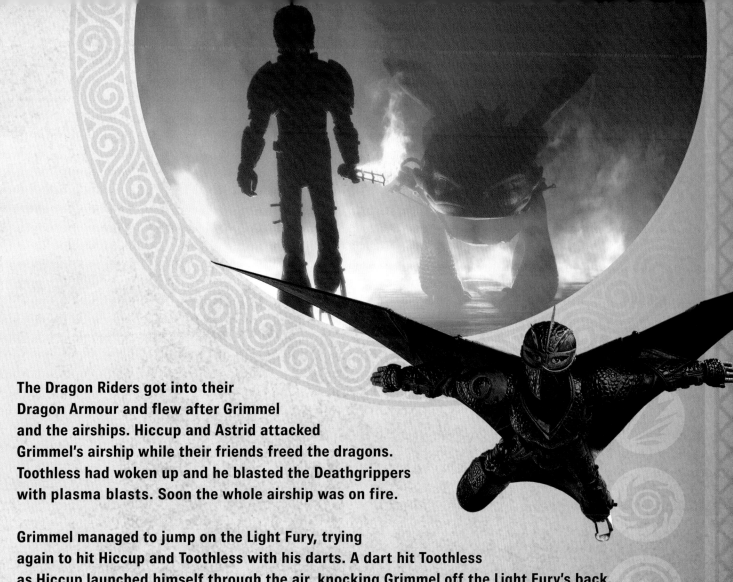

The Dragon Riders got into their
Dragon Armour and flew after Grimmel
and the airships. Hiccup and Astrid attacked
Grimmel's airship while their friends freed the dragons.
Toothless had woken up and he blasted the Deathgrippers
with plasma blasts. Soon the whole airship was on fire.

Grimmel managed to jump on the Light Fury, trying
again to hit Hiccup and Toothless with his darts. A dart hit Toothless
as Hiccup launched himself through the air, knocking Grimmel off the Light Fury's back.

"Save Toothless!" cried Hiccup as they all plunged into the sea.

The Light Fury dived down to rescue Toothless, returning quickly to pick up Hiccup.
Grimmel fell into the water.

Everyone returned to New Berk, happy to have defeated Grimmel
and to have saved their friends.

But Hiccup knew that it couldn't last. The dragons would never
be safe as long as there were people like Grimmel around to hunt them.

"I won't hold you back anymore," Hiccup told Toothless.
"You've looked after us long enough."

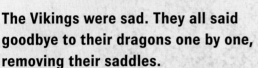

The Vikings were sad. They all said goodbye to their dragons one by one, removing their saddles.

Toothless didn't want to leave his friend, but Hiccup turned to the Light Fury.

"He is all yours," he said. Toothless and the Light Fury were happy.

"Lead them to the Hidden World," said Hiccup. "You'll all be safer there."

Toothless nodded and roared. The other dragons took to the skies and headed for the Hidden World.

Ten years later, Hiccup, Astrid and their children sailed to the caldera to see their dragon friends. When they arrived at the Hidden World, they found that Toothless and the Light Fury had baby dragons, whom they called Night Lights. The Night Lights played happily together, without fear of dragon trappers. Hiccup was so happy to know the dragons were still safe and thriving in the Hidden World.

QUICK-FIRE QUIZ

It's time to put your dragons knowledge to the test with this quick-fire quiz! How many can you answer correctly?

1 Which Dragon Rider was once a trapper?

....

2 What's the name of Hiccup's mother?

....

3 What do the Vikings call their new home?

....

4 Name the new dragon species with white shimmering scales.

....

5 Which Viking does Stormfly ride with?

....

6 Where is the Hidden World?

....

7 Who is the Alpha dragon?

....

8 What are the names of the Viking twins?

....

9 What is the species of Grimmel's fearsome dragons?

....

10 Why did the Vikings leave Berk?

....

Answers on page 68.

TAKE FLIGHT

Toothless is trying to follow his new friend, Light Fury, to the Hidden World. Unscramble the paths to work out which one leads to Light Fury.

1

2

3

Answers on page 68.

FISHLEGS' DRAGON FACTS

ADULT SUPERVISION NEEDED

Carefully cut out your dragon cards, you never know when you might encounter an unknown dragon!

Fishlegs knows everything there is to know about dragons and keeps all their information on these handy fact cards. Perfect for a fire-breathing situation!

DRAGON CLASS

The Vikings group every dragon into one of seven 'classes'. Sometimes dragons move into different classes when Fishlegs discovers more about them.

SHARP CLASS

Sharp Class dragons have razor-sharp wings and tails!

STRIKE CLASS

Supersonic speed. Silent stealth. Strike Class dragons include the most powerful – and most famous – type of dragon to roam the earth.

STOKER CLASS

Where Stoker Class dragons breathe, flames and ashes follow. Some of these dragons have even been known to set themselves on fire!

MYSTERY CLASS

Shrouded in secrets, much is still unknown about Mystery Class dragons.

TRACKER CLASS

Above the clouds, across Berk or inside the Hidden World, Tracker Class dragons can pinpoint any Viking or dragon with astounding accuracy.

BOULDER CLASS

Loyal defenders of the earth, Boulder Class dragons will do anything – from spewing lava to blasting the bumps off their rugged exteriors – in order to protect their land and their friends.

TIDAL CLASS

Tidal Class dragons reign over the sea, often causing fear in their wake.

NIGHT FURY
FAST AND FEARLESS ALPHA DRAGON

LENGTH: 26 ft   **WINGSPAN:** 45 ft
WEIGHT: 1,776 lbs

ATTACK	15	
SPEED	20	
ARMOUR	18	
FIREPOWER	14	
SHOT LIMIT	6	
VENOM	0	
JAW STRENGTH	6	
STEALTH	18	

ABILITIES: dive-bombing, blasting plasma, flying at supersonic speeds, navigating in the dark by using echolocation

PERSONALITY: fiercely loyal, intelligent

OTHER FACTS: Night Furies are the fastest dragons in the sky, along with Light Furies

LIGHT FURY
IRIDESCENCE IN THE SKY

LENGTH: 22 ft   **WINGSPAN:** 42 ft
WEIGHT: 1,600 lbs

ATTACK	15	
SPEED	20	
ARMOUR	18	
FIREPOWER	14	
SHOT LIMIT	6	
VENOM	0	
JAW STRENGTH	6	
STEALTH	18	

ABILITIES: blasting plasma, flying at supersonic speeds, appearing invisible by flying through their own plasma blasts

PERSONALITY: shy, empathetic

OTHER FACTS: Just like Night Furies blend into the night sky, Light Furies can easily hide among the clouds and sky during daylight

DEADLY NADDER
LETHAL BEAUTY

LENGTH: 30 ft   **WINGSPAN:** 42 ft
WEIGHT: 2,628 lbs

ATTACK	10	
SPEED	8	
ARMOUR	16	
FIREPOWER	18	
SHOT LIMIT	6	
VENOM	16	
JAW STRENGTH	5	
STEALTH	10	

ABILITIES: shooting spikes from their hides and tails, tracking scents

PERSONALITY: fastidious, playful

OTHER FACTS: Deadly Nadder's magnesium fire is the hottest of any dragon

HIDEOUS ZIPPLEBACK
TWO HEADS ARE (MAYBE) BETTER THAN ONE

LENGTH: 66 ft   **WINGSPAN:** 38 ft
WEIGHT: 6,036 lbs

ATTACK	12	
SPEED	10	
ARMOUR	10	
FIREPOWER	14	
SHOT LIMIT	6	
VENOM	0	
JAW STRENGTH	6	(3 x 2)
STEALTH	22	(11 x 2)

ABILITIES: one head breathing gas and the other head igniting it with a spark to create explosive fire

PERSONALITY: the different heads do not often get along or want to go in the same direction

OTHER FACTS: Hideous Zipplebacks can transform into wheels of fire by grabbing their tails and spinning like bowling balls

LIGHT FURY

STRIKE CLASS

TOOTHLESS

STRIKE CLASS

NAME
BARF AND BELCH

MYSTERY CLASS

NAME
STORMFLY

TRACKER CLASS

CUT ALONG HERE

6

GRONCKLE
SOLID AS A ROCK

LENGTH: 14 ft **WINGSPAN:** 18 ft
WEIGHT: 5,724 lbs

ATTACK	8	
SPEED	4	
ARMOUR	20	
FIREPOWER	14	
SHOT LIMIT	6	
VENOM	0	
JAW STRENGTH	8	
STEALTH	5	

- **ABILITIES:** shooting flaming chunks of rock and lava
- **PERSONALITY:** sweet, sensitive, and cautious
- **OTHER FACTS:** Gronckles are the only dragons that can fly backwards and sideways

MONSTROUS NIGHTMARE
THIS DRAGON IS ON FIRE!

LENGTH: 61 ft **WINGSPAN:** 68 ft
WEIGHT: 5,040 lbs

ATTACK	15	
SPEED	16	
ARMOUR	12	
FIREPOWER	15	
SHOT LIMIT	10	
VENOM	0	
JAW STRENGTH	6	
STEALTH	9	

- **ABILITIES:** self-immolating (covering their body with fire)
- **PERSONALITY:** impulsive, easily agitated
- **OTHER FACTS:** Monstrous Nightmares light themselves on fire by emitting kerosene from their pores, then breathing fire to set it all aflame

STORMCUTTER
FOUR-WINGED FORCE OF NATURE

LENGTH: 31 ft 3 1/4 ins
WINGSPAN: 48 ft diagonally
WEIGHT: 2,500 lbs

ATTACK	10	
SPEED	17	
ARMOUR	4	
FIREPOWER	12	
SHOT LIMIT	8	
VENOM	0	
JAW STRENGTH	5	
STEALTH	13	

- **ABILITIES:** X-wing flying, shooting fire in a spiral shape
- **PERSONALITY:** intelligent, playful, sensitive, powerful
- **OTHER FACTS:** Stormcutters have two sets of wings, allowing them to brake in mid-air

BEWILDERBEAST
KIND-HEARTED PROTECTOR

LENGTH: 520 ft **WINGSPAN:** 150 ft
WEIGHT: 100 tons / 200,000 lbs

ATTACK	50	
SPEED	6 on land / 18 underwater	
ARMOUR	38	
FIREPOWER	60	
SHOT LIMIT	8	
VENOM	0	
JAW STRENGTH	48	
STEALTH	2	

- **ABILITIES:** blasting massive sprays of ice, intimidating others with their size
- **PERSONALITY:** kind and docile, ruling all dragons without harm
- **OTHER FACTS:** Bewilderbeasts are the biggest sea dragons

CUT ALONG HERE

NAME
HOOKFANG

NAME
MEATLUG

STOKER CLASS

BOULDER CLASS

NAME
BEWILDERBEAST

NAME
CLOUDJUMPER

TIDAL CLASS

SHARP CLASS

CUT ALONG HERE

DEATHGRIPPER
UNBRIDLED DRAGON KILLERS

LENGTH: 28 ft **WINGSPAN:** 32 ft
WEIGHT: 2,100 lbs

ATTACK	27	
SPEED	12	
ARMOUR	20	
FIREPOWER	12	
SHOT LIMIT	8	
VENOM	12	
JAW STRENGTH	16	
STEALTH	6	

ABILITIES: hunting Vikings and dragons, attacking with their tusks and pincers, striking with their poisonous clubbed tail

PERSONALITY: brutal

OTHER FACTS: Deathgrippers have a fascinating control over their own venom. One strike from a Deathgripper's tail paralyzes its prey. A second strike puts it out of its misery. A third strike makes the body of the prey poisonous to the touch

RUMBLEHORN
BLOODHOUND OF DRAGONS

LENGTH: 11 ft 1/2 ins
WINGSPAN: 30 ft **WEIGHT:** 1,100 lbs

ATTACK	11	
SPEED	7	
ARMOUR	12	
FIREPOWER	22	
SHOT LIMIT	4	
VENOM	0	
JAW STRENGTH	5	
STEALTH	6	

ABILITIES: ramming with their axe-shaped heads, tracking scents

PERSONALITY: intelligent, stealthy, flexible

OTHER FACTS: Rumblehorns are so heavy that they can tip over a ship while flying at full speed

HOTBURPLE
LARGE, SNORING OAF OF A DRAGON

LENGTH: 14 ft **WINGSPAN:** 18 ft
WEIGHT: 5,724 lbs

ATTACK	8	
SPEED	4	
ARMOUR	20	
FIREPOWER	14	
SHOT LIMIT	6	
VENOM	0	
JAW STRENGTH	8	
STEALTH	5	

ABILITIES: shooting flaming chunks of rock and lava

PERSONALITY: lazy, fussy, difficult to keep awake

OTHER FACTS: Hotburples sometimes fall asleep while flying in midair

NIGHT LIGHTS
ADORABLE OFFSPRING OF THE NIGHT FURY AND THE LIGHT FURY

LENGTH: up to 24 ft
WINGSPAN: up to 44 ft
WEIGHT: up to 1,700 lbs

ATTACK	15*	
SPEED	20*	
ARMOUR	18*	
FIREPOWER	14*	
SHOT LIMIT	6*	
VENOM	0	
JAW STRENGTH	6*	
STEALTH	18*	

*ADULT NIGHT LIGHTS

ABILITIES: cloaking themselves by using their own fire blasts to transform their scales into mirror-like reflectors

PERSONALITY: playful and curious

OTHER FACTS: just like the Night Fury and the Light Fury, Night Lights have retractable teeth

NAME
SKULLCRUSHER

NAME
DEATH GRIPPER

NAME
NIGHT LIGHTS

NAME
HOTBURPLE

CUT ALONG HERE

FLYING FRIENDS

The Vikings and the dragons are off to find a new home, and probably save some dragons on the way! Draw lines between each rider and his or her dragon. One dragon does not have a match – circle this one.

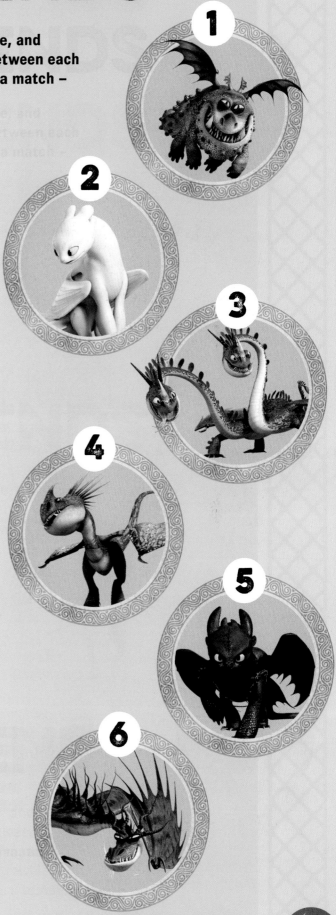

A

B

C

D

E

1

2

3

4

5

6

Answers on page 68.

OFF TO BATTLE

Colour in the picture below of the
Dragon Riders preparing to capture
Grimmel, the feared dragon hunter.

DRAGON MIX-UP

Unscramble these words to spell out the names of your favourite dragons.

1. HETTSSOOL

2. MYRTOSLF

3. FABR DNA BLCHE

SECRET MESSAGE

Every time a double letter appears cross it out. Then write every letter that remains in the circles below to reveal your secret message.

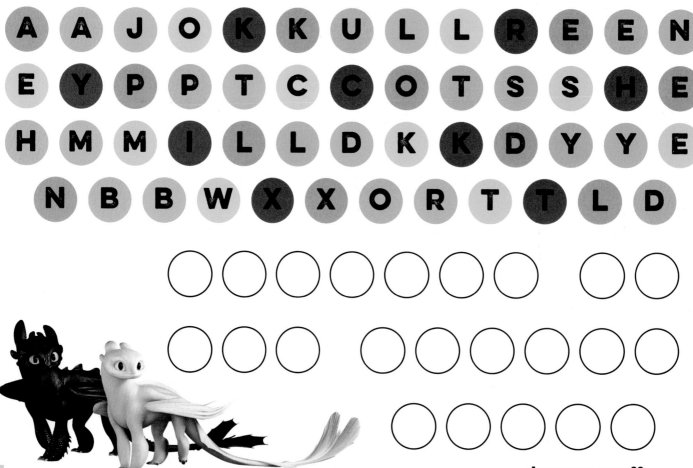

Answers on page 68.

MATCH THE PAIR

Are you a keen dragon spotter like Fishlegs? There are five versions of Stormfly on this page. See if you can spot which two are the matching pair.

1

2

3

4

5

Answers on page 68.

DRAW TOOTHLESS

The Night Fury is the most dangerous of all the dragons. Do you dare to draw one yourself? Use this picture of Toothless to help you.

Now you've studied Fishlegs' fact cards and learnt all about the dragons of Berk and beyond, it's time to create your own. Will it have horns, multiple heads or even breathe ice? Use these dragons as inspiration.

COMPLETE THE SEQUENCE

There are lots of dragons in Berk and Fishlegs loves to study them for his dragon cards. Help him finish the sequences by drawing the missing dragons in the boxes below.

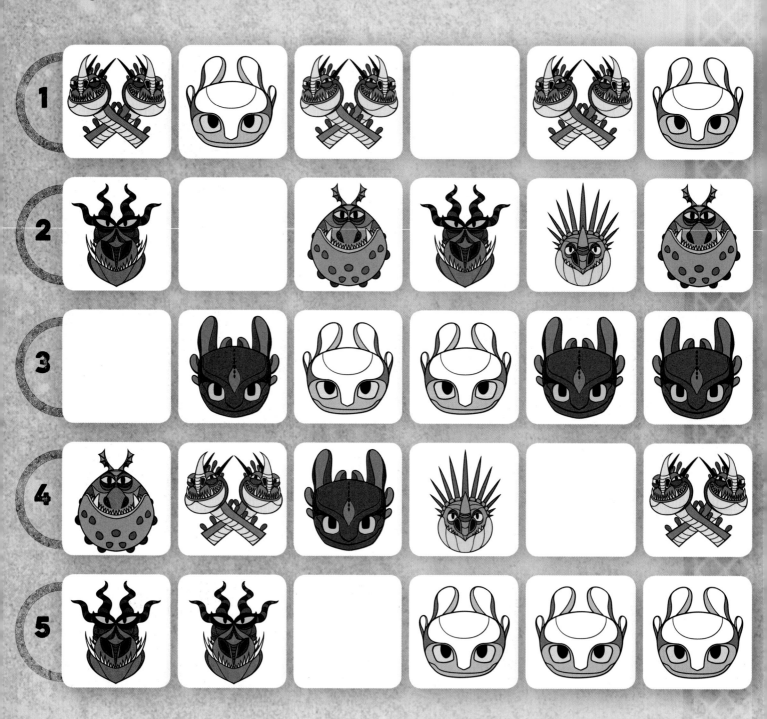

Answers on page 68.

HIGH FLYING!

CUT ALONG HERE

SHAPES AND SIZES

The dragons of New Berk come in all shapes and sizes. But which is the biggest? Put these in order beginning with the smallest.

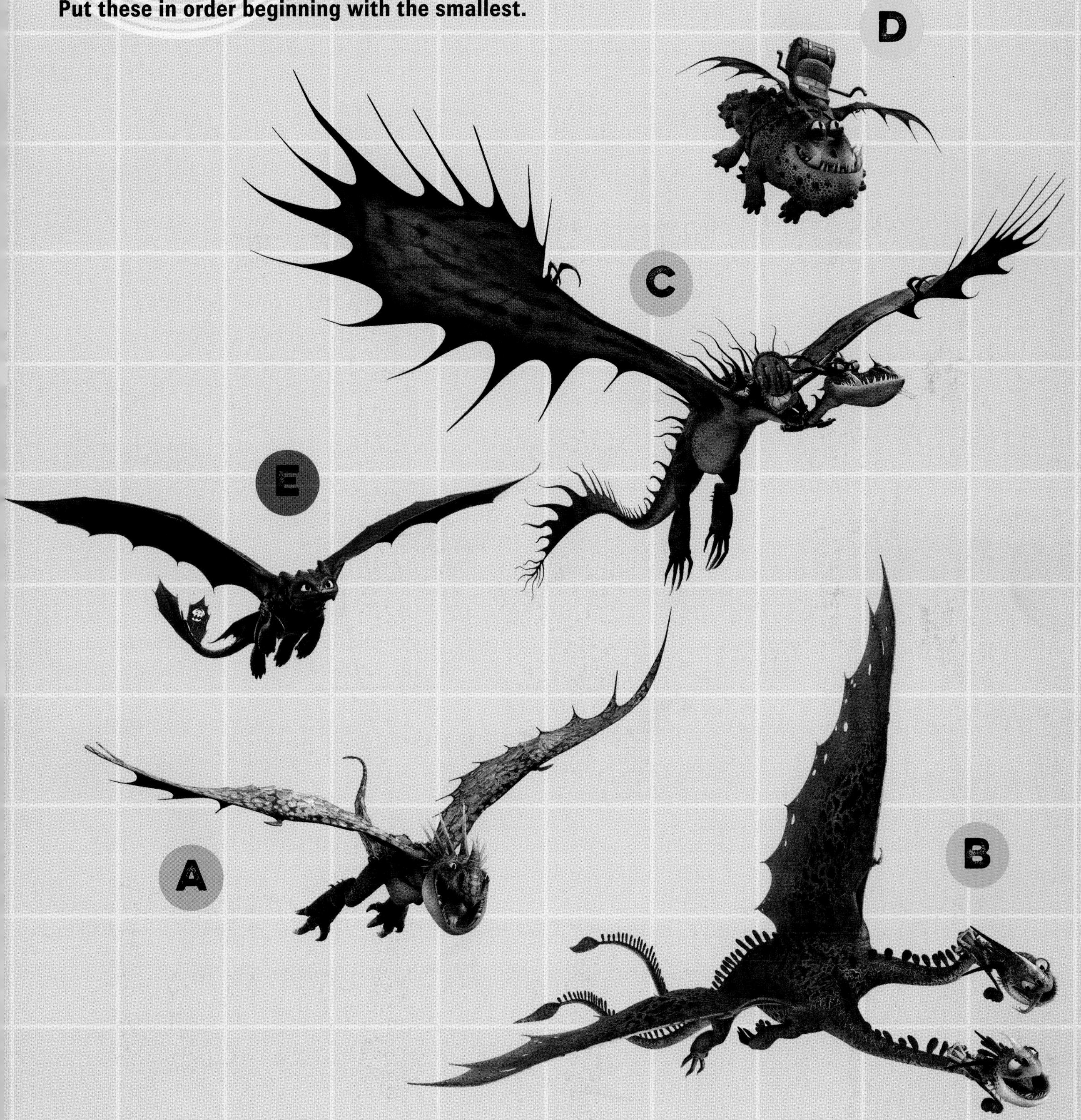

D

C

E

A

B

SMALLEST ⟶ LARGEST

Answers on page 68.

ANSWERS

PAGE 16 - DRAGON MAZE

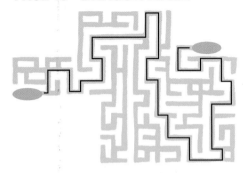

PAGE 21 - SUDOKU

2	4	3	1
1	3	4	2
3	2	1	4
4	1	2	3

PAGE 22 - SPOT THE DIFFERENCE

PAGE 23 - PICTURE MIX-UP
1 - C, 2 - A, 3 - D,
4 - F, 5 - B, 6 - E.

PAGE 30 - THE DRAGONS OF BERK SEARCH AND FIND
9 white sheep, 1 black sheep

PAGE 30 - ODD DRAGON OUT

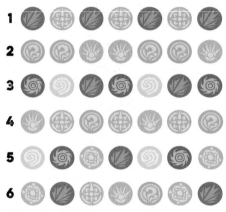

PAGE 34 - WHICH VIKING IS THIS?
Eret

PAGE 39 - BERK SEARCH

F	N	G	N	A	F	K	O	O	H	E	N
R	M	A	L	S	S	E	D	O	P	G	A
A	U	S	N	O	T	L	O	U	T	R	D
B	S	T	K	J	X	P	U	C	C	I	H
H	T	O	X	U	E	E	Y	S	R	M	E
R	G	R	T	H	A	E	R	T	H	M	L
I	U	M	U	W	O	F	S	N	M	E	P
B	L	F	N	O	V	A	L	K	A	L	T
H	T	L	F	S	G	E	L	H	S	I	F
P	A	Y	F	N	D	H	C	L	E	B	K
L	E	W	U	T	U	R	G	A	T	M	E
S	M	X	T	O	O	T	H	L	E	S	S

PAGE 40 - DANCE OF THE DRAGONS
1 - 6, 2 - red, 3 - 12,
4 - 2, 5 - Green

PAGE 48 - QUICK QUIZ
1 Eret
2 Valka
3 New Berk
4 Light Fury
5 Astrid
6 Under the ocean
7 Toothless
8 Tuffnut and Ruffnut
9 Deathgripper dragons
10 To save the dragons

PAGE 49 - TAKE FLIGHT
Path 2 leads to Light Fury

PAGE 57 - FLYING FRIENDS
A - 4, B - 5, C - 6, D - 1, E - 3.
Light Fury - she has no rider.

PAGE 60 - DRAGON MIX-UP
A Toothless
B Stormfly
C Barf and Belch

PAGE 60 - SECRET MESSAGE
JOURNEY TO THE HIDDEN WORLD

PAGE 61 - MATCH THE PAIR
Pictures 2 and 4 are the same

PAGE 64 - COMPLETE THE SEQUENCE

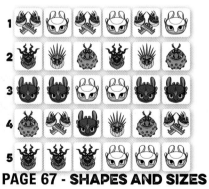

PAGE 67 - SHAPES AND SIZES

D E A C B
SMALLEST ⟶ LARGEST

BEST BUDS!